Grab a pen and write on with CGP!

This CGP book is perfect for helping Year 6 pupils improve their writing — it's packed with guided activities based on a wide range of styles and genres, plus 'extra challenge' questions to get them writing independently.

Answers to every question are included in a cut-out-and-keep section, so it's easy to keep track of how pupils are getting on.

You can also download free annotated examples of a range of text types to give pupils ideas for their own writing. You'll find them here:

www.cgpbooks.co.uk/KS2WritingResources

What CGP is all about

Our sole aim here at CGP is to produce the highest quality books — carefully written, immaculately presented and dangerously close to being funny.

Then we work our socks off to get them out to you — at the cheapest possible prices.

Contents

The exercises in this book cover different types of writing, and different techniques you can use to make your writing effective. Use the contents below to see what's covered where.

Published by CGP

Editors: Claire Boulter, Andy Cashmore, Jenny Underwood

Contributors: Samantha Bensted, Alison Griffin, Amanda MacNaughton, Maxine Petrie

With thanks to Emma Crighton for the proofreading.

With thanks to Emily Smith for the copyright research.

ISBN: 978 1 78294 957 2

Thumb illustration used throughout the book © iStock.com.

Images and clipart throughout the book from Corel® and clipart.com

Image on page 25 © [illegible]Tromber. Licensed under the Creative Commons Attribution-Share Alike 4.0 International license: https://creativecommons.org/licenses/by-sa/4.0/deed.en

With thanks to iStock.com for permission to use the image on page 34.

Printed by Elanders Ltd, Newcastle upon Tyne.

Based on the classic CGP style created by Richard Parsons.

Planning Your Writing

Before you start a piece of writing, you need to plan your work — this includes thinking about the purpose and audience. The purpose and audience of your text affect the language you use — e.g. if you were writing to the Queen, you would use formal language.

Plans can be in note form — you don't need to use full sentences.

Planning also includes thinking about how to structure your writing — e.g. how to start and end your text and what order your ideas should come in.

Key Terms

The purpose of a text is the reason why it's been written.	e.g. a letter to persuade the reader to sponsor you.
The audience is the person or people who the text is aimed at.	e.g. an article for teenagers, a letter to a friend

1 **Draw lines to match each extract to its purpose and then to its audience.**

Extract	Purpose	Audience
Although your GCSE exams aren't until next term, it's never too early to start revising. Setting aside half an hour a day to revise tricky topics could be the difference between passing and failing.	To persuade	Children
The furry, purple monster stomped along the road. Cars swerved to avoid him, and a passing policeman blew his whistle. The monster ignored them all.	To entertain	Adults
Why should you employ me as pudding taster at your restaurant? I believe that I would be successful in the role because I am hard-working, enthusiastic and passionate about pudding.	To advise	Teenagers

2 **Draw a line to match each text to the most appropriate style of writing.**

A newspaper article informing readers about a war.	Descriptive language, building suspense.
An email telling your best friend about your holiday.	Formal, serious language, lots of information.
A story about a night in a haunted house.	Informal language, personal tone.

3 **This is a plan for a report about castles, but the points are out of order. Rearrange them to put the plan in a sensible order.**

You don't need to write each point out in full — just the bit in bold.

Earliest castles — earth mounds, wooden keeps

Introduction — what castles are, why they were built, where they were built

Conclusion — many castles still standing, successful defensive structures

Late Medieval castles — stone keeps, defensive walls, other defences

Decline of castles — little defence against cannons. Some castles were abandoned and fell into ruin

....

....

....

....

....

© ValeryEgorov/iStock Editorial / Getty Images Plus

....

....

4 **This is part of a plan for a story. Complete the plan by writing brief notes about what will happen in the middle of the story.**

Beginning — Lian hears a strange noise coming from the shed.

....

....

....

....

....

....

End — Lian goes back to her house for tea.

What is making the noise?

What happens in the shed?

What problem must Lian solve?

5 **This is part of a plan for a newspaper report about the theft of a valuable dog. Complete the plan by writing what the middle of the article will include. In the box below the plan, write the main purpose and audience of the article.**

Headline — Pet Pilferer Pinches Prize Pooch

Introduction — Summary of what happened, to who, when, where and why.

Paragraph 1 — ....

Paragraph 2 — ....

Paragraph 3 — ....

Conclusion — Investigation continues to find the culprit.

Purpose — ....

Audience — ....

★ Extra Challenge

Plan a newspaper article about a meteor landing in your area.

"I can plan fiction and non-fiction texts."

Editing Your Work

Every piece of writing you do needs to be edited. This means reading it carefully to check whether it's suitable for the audience and purpose, how well it flows and whether it makes sense.

It's also a chance to make it better in other ways — for example, by choosing more interesting words or adding suspense.

Reading your work aloud can help you see how it could be improved.

1. This is the first draft of the start of a fantasy story. Some suggestions have been written on it in red. Read the extract, and then read the suggestions.

Bill was a ten-year-old boy. He lived in a house with
Is this needed? More interesting to start with Bill doing something.
his mum and his baby brother. One day, Bill saw
Add some description of the setting and/or the cat.
a cat sitting on a fence. The cat was injured. Bill
Make clear what injury it had.
stopped and looked at the cat and it looked back at
More interesting to write what it said.
him and it started to talk. Bill was very surprised
Show his surprise.
that the cat could talk.

You can make other changes too — not just those suggested.

Rewrite the extract, using the suggestions to make it better.

....

....

....

....

....

....

....

2 **Here is a second draft of the opening of the story on the previous page. Write on it some extra suggestions that would make it better.**

One day, Bill was walking along the tree-lined road on his way to school when he saw a fluffy cat at the side of the road. The cat was holding its paw in the air and it had a splinter in it. Bill stopped and looked at the cat and it looked back at him.

"What are you looking at, two-legs?" the cat said.

Bill gasped and stared at the cat.

★ Extra Challenge

Write a third draft of the opening, including the changes you've suggested.

3 **This is an extract from a report about coral reefs. Read it carefully and write on it some suggestions that would make it better.**

The Great Barrier Reef is in Australia. The biggest coral reef in the world is the Great Barrier Reef. It started growing over 20 000 years ago.

Lots of fish and sea creatures live in the Great Barrier Reef. There are turtles, dolphins, whales, sharks and fish. There are also sea snakes and they can live underwater and they can also bite people.

The Great Barrier Reef is over 2000 km long. It is actually around 3000 smaller reefs that make up the Great Barrier Reef.

★ Extra Challenge

Rewrite the extract to include the changes you've suggested. Swap it with a friend and edit each other's work.

"I can edit my work to make it better."

Proofreading Your Work

When you've finished editing your writing, you should proofread it. This means looking for mistakes in spelling, punctuation and grammar, as well as any incorrect facts or places where the writing isn't clear.

1 **This is a late draft of a letter persuading an author to visit a school. Read it carefully. Circle each mistake and write the correction above it.**

Deer Miss Henshaw,

We would like to invite you to visit our school and give a tolk to our class. Everyone in our class love your book's, espesially the 'Broken Wings' series. We have been doing a project based on the first 'Broken Wings' book 'Flying Free'. We prefer it than any other book, and we have learnt a lot about flying machines

So, why should you visit us. You should visit because we will make you feel really welcome, with handmade banners and an delicious lunch in our cantine. We had also planned lots of activites so you will have a wonderfull day. furthermore, you have inspired us too write our own stories, and we would be overjoyed to have the chance to share them with u.

Your visit would have made us elated, excited and motivated to keep writeing. So please consider coming to visit, it would make our year!

Your sincerely,

Class 6B

"I can proofread my work and correct mistakes."

All About Volcanoes

When you write a non-fiction text, it should be accurate and informative.

To make your text sound reliable, use an objective tone and technical terms. Generalisations can also help to make your writing more informative.

Key Terms

- Writing with an objective tone means giving facts rather than opinions and not using first person pronouns, such as 'I' and 'we'. — e.g. 'Cats are popular pets' instead of 'I think cats make the best pets'.
- Technical terms are the specialist words you use about a topic. — e.g. Plants make their food using photosynthesis.
- A generalisation is something that is true in most cases. — e.g. Otters often sleep holding hands.

1 **Read this extract from a report about volcanoes. Underline all the facts.**

Active volcanoes are found all around the world, although fortunately there are none in the UK. Volcanoes are the scariest thing ever: in my lifetime alone, they have caused destruction in many countries. However, they are also beautiful, and lots of tourists visit them.

A fact is a piece of information that you can prove to be true.

Rewrite the extract using only facts. Use an objective tone.

Don't use first person pronouns — e.g. write 'It is thought...' instead of 'I think...'

....

....

....

....

2 **Fill in the gaps to turn these sentences into generalisations. Use the words in the box or come up with your own.**

You use generalisations when writing about something that's usually (but not always) true.

.... volcanoes are located in inhabited areas,

so when they erupt they .... cause

a lot of destruction. ...., lava flows

and falling debris destroy buildings and kill people.

Plants and animals close to volcanoes are also

.... harmed by eruptions.

some	often
frequently	
as a rule	
in many cases	
many	most

3 **This is a diagram from the report. Circle the technical term for each part of the volcano.**

Technical terms are often complex scientific words.

Ash cloud / Fog

Main vent / Big tube

Big hole / Crater

Fiery liquid / Lava flow

Magma chamber / Pit of hot rock

Thin tube / Secondary vent

Using technical terms from the diagram, write a section for the report about the different parts of a volcano.

Think about how to structure your writing, e.g. what order to write about the parts of the volcano in.

....

....

....

....

....

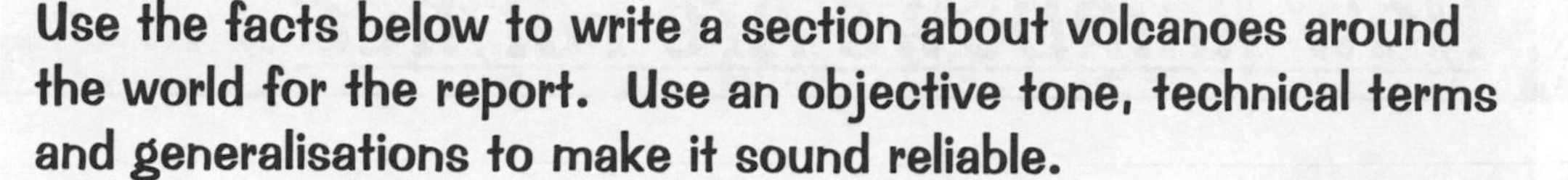

4 **Use the facts below to write a section about volcanoes around the world for the report. Use an objective tone, technical terms and generalisations to make it sound reliable.**

Volcanoes Around the World

- Over 1500 active volcanoes on Earth.
- General location: along plate margins.
- 75% of active volcanoes are in the Ring of Fire, an area of the Pacific Ocean.
- Country with highest number of volcanoes: USA.
- World's largest above-water volcano: Mauna Loa, Hawaii, USA (4169 m high).

★ Extra Challenge

Write a short report about something you know a lot about — for example, a hobby, your favourite team or an animal. Use an objective tone, technical terms and generalisations.

"I can use an objective tone, technical terms and generalisations to write informative texts."

How Rainbows Are Formed

Your writing needs to flow so that the reader can follow your points easily.

To help your writing flow, you can use pronouns and linking words and phrases to join your sentences and paragraphs. Adverbials of time and place can do this too, and they can also be used to add extra information to texts.

Grammar Guide

- **Pronouns** are words that replace nouns. e.g. The parrot sang. It also danced.
- **Linking words and phrases** join together clauses, sentences and paragraphs. e.g. The parrot sang because it enjoyed showing off.
- **Adverbials** usually describe verbs. They can give you more information about when or where something is happening. e.g. The parrot sang this morning. e.g. The parrot sang in the corner of the room.

1 **Read this extract from a text explaining how rainbows form. Underline the places where the text would flow better if repeated nouns were replaced with pronouns.**

Have you ever wondered how rainbows appear in the sky as rainbows do? Do you want to know why rainbows need rain to get rainbows' colours or the role sunlight plays in forming rainbows? If so, read on to learn what a rainbow is and how a rainbow is formed.

Rewrite the extract using pronouns.

....

....

....

....

....

....

Is what you've written easier to read than the first extract? Why is this?

2 **Complete each adverbial of time or place so it provides extra information about how rainbows form. Use the words and phrases in the box below.**

Rainbows appear .... when sunlight passes through water droplets. Beams of light that come .... are .... white, but this white light is made up of many different colours. .... the white light passes through water, it slows down and scatters .... This causes the different colours to become visible.

in the sky	when	initially
in different directions		from the sun

★ Extra Challenge

Write a short explanation of your morning routine, using adverbials of time and place.

3 **Circle the correct linking word or phrase in bold to help the text flow.**

Rainbows are formed due to the combination of sunlight and water droplets. **As a result / Equally**, rainbows only remain while there is moisture in the atmosphere. **Consequently / Nevertheless**, they tend to be short-lived. **Therefore / However**, in some cases rainbows can persist for longer.

For example / In contrast, long-lasting rainbows can form near waterfalls **because / unless** the spray from them provides a constant source of water droplets for sunlight to pass through.

4 **This is a picture of a strange invention. Explain what it does and how to use it. Use pronouns, adverbials and linking words and phrases to make your text flow.**

Think about what the invention might do — does it produce rainbows or let you travel to other worlds?

Make sure your explanation follows a logical order. Use adverbials of time, such as 'before', 'after' and 'first', to make the order clear.

Remember to give the invention a name. Use pronouns so you don't have to keep referring to it by name.

Think about what do you have to do to make the invention work. Use linking words to make your explanation clear and adverbials to add extra information.

★ Extra Challenge

Read what you've written. Mark any places where extra pronouns, adverbials and linking words could usefully be added.

"I can link sentences and paragraphs to make my text flow."

Should Schools Ban Unhealthy Food?

If you want to write a balanced discussion on a topic, you can use arguments and counter-arguments that rely on facts, rather than opinions.

You can use linking words and phrases to help your discussion flow.

Key Terms

An argument is writing that supports a particular view.	e.g. Animals should not be kept in zoos because they cannot roam freely.
A counter-argument is writing that supports the opposite view to the argument.	e.g. Animals should be kept in zoos to help conserve rare species.
Linking words and phrases are used to join together clauses, sentences or paragraphs.	e.g. Some people like jam on their eggs. However, many people do not.

Opinions are people's views or beliefs. E.g. 'Football is fun' is an opinion.

1 This is the start of a discussion about whether schools should ban junk food. It contains facts and opinions. Underline the opinions.

Unhealthy food is often high in salt, sugar and fat. It is also delicious. Some people think that schools should not serve unhealthy food because it can cause health problems and encourage poor eating habits. Those people are wrong: children should have the freedom to make their own decisions about their diet.

Rewrite the text, changing the opinions to facts.

You can change an opinion to a fact by making it clear that it is an opinion. E.g. 'Chips are tasty' is an opinion, but 'Many people think that chips are tasty' is a fact.

....

....

....

....

....

....

2 **In the next part of the text, add a linking word or phrase to each gap to help the text flow.**

Add punctuation if it's needed.

It is widely known that a poor diet can have a negative effect on health. .... too much salt can cause high blood pressure, increasing the risk of heart disease. .... a diet high in sugar can cause tooth decay and may contribute to liver damage.

.... if unhealthy food is banned in schools, children may simply eat more of it outside of school. .... it would be better if they learnt to eat unhealthy food in small quantities, rather than it being banned entirely.

3 **Below are some arguments in favour of banning junk food in schools. For each one, write a counter-argument against banning junk food.**

Children who have no choice but to eat healthily at school may discover healthy foods that they enjoy, improving their diet in the long term.

....

....

By encouraging children to eat fruit and vegetables, schools can ensure that children have all the vitamins and minerals they need.

....

....

....

★ Extra Challenge

Write an argument and a counter-argument for a discussion about whether children should have to wear school uniform. Make sure you use linking words.

4 Below are some more points for and against schools banning unhealthy food. Use these or your own points to continue the discussion text.

Children can be taught the benefits of a healthy diet, so they choose healthy options.

Young children may not fully understand the benefits of healthy eating.

Children have the right to choose what they eat.

Banning junk food may decrease childhood obesity and related health problems, e.g. high blood pressure.

Think about how to structure your writing — for example, you could give an argument and then a counter-argument. Use linking words and phrases to make your points flow.

★ Extra Challenge

Write a conclusion to the text. It should sum up both sides of the issue and make a recommendation of what should be done.

"I can write a balanced discussion that flows well."

A Letter of Complaint

When you write for a serious purpose, or an audience who you don't know well, you don't want it to sound chatty and personal. Instead, it should be formal and polite.

You can make your writing more formal by changing the words and sentence structures that you use.

Key Terms

- Formal writing is serious and impersonal. It often uses sentences with several clauses. — e.g. The art contest, which will be judged next week, will benefit the school.
- Informal writing is more chatty and personal. It often uses sentences with only one clause. — e.g. I reckon the art contest will be fab for our school.
- A clause is a bit of a sentence that contains a verb and someone doing the action. — e.g. Samia kicked the ball.

1 **This is an extract from a letter complaining about a trip to a funfair. Circle the correct options from the words in bold to make the letter formal.**

My friend and I / Me and my mate visited your fair last week, and it was **a rubbish / an unpleasant** experience. **For starters / To begin with**, we queued for **a long time / ages** to buy tickets. This was **well / very** irritating. To make matters worse, when we **made it to / reached** the front of the queue, the ticket seller was **irritable / huffy** because we did not have the correct change. His attitude **tainted our enjoyment of / messed up** the day.

2 **Read the next part of the letter. Underline all the informal words and phrases.**

Personal pronouns like 'I' and 'we' can be used in a letter.

Inside, we discovered that most of the rides were busted. Loads of them appeared to be unsafe: we noticed rust on the carousel, and the Ferris wheel was all smashed up. It is vital that stuff be repaired soon.

We also bought some hot dogs, which turned out to be as tough as old boots. This was a downer as we were proper hungry.

Rewrite this part of the letter to make it formal.

....

....

....

....

....

....

....

....

3 **Add a clause to each of these sentences from the letter to give extra information. Use formal language.**

We queued for an hour for the dodgems, ...

It was a hot day ...., which made our wait more uncomfortable. ...., my dodgem broke down after two minutes. ...., we were very frustrated.

4 The man in this picture has had a bad experience of something. Write down what you think he is saying in the speech bubble.

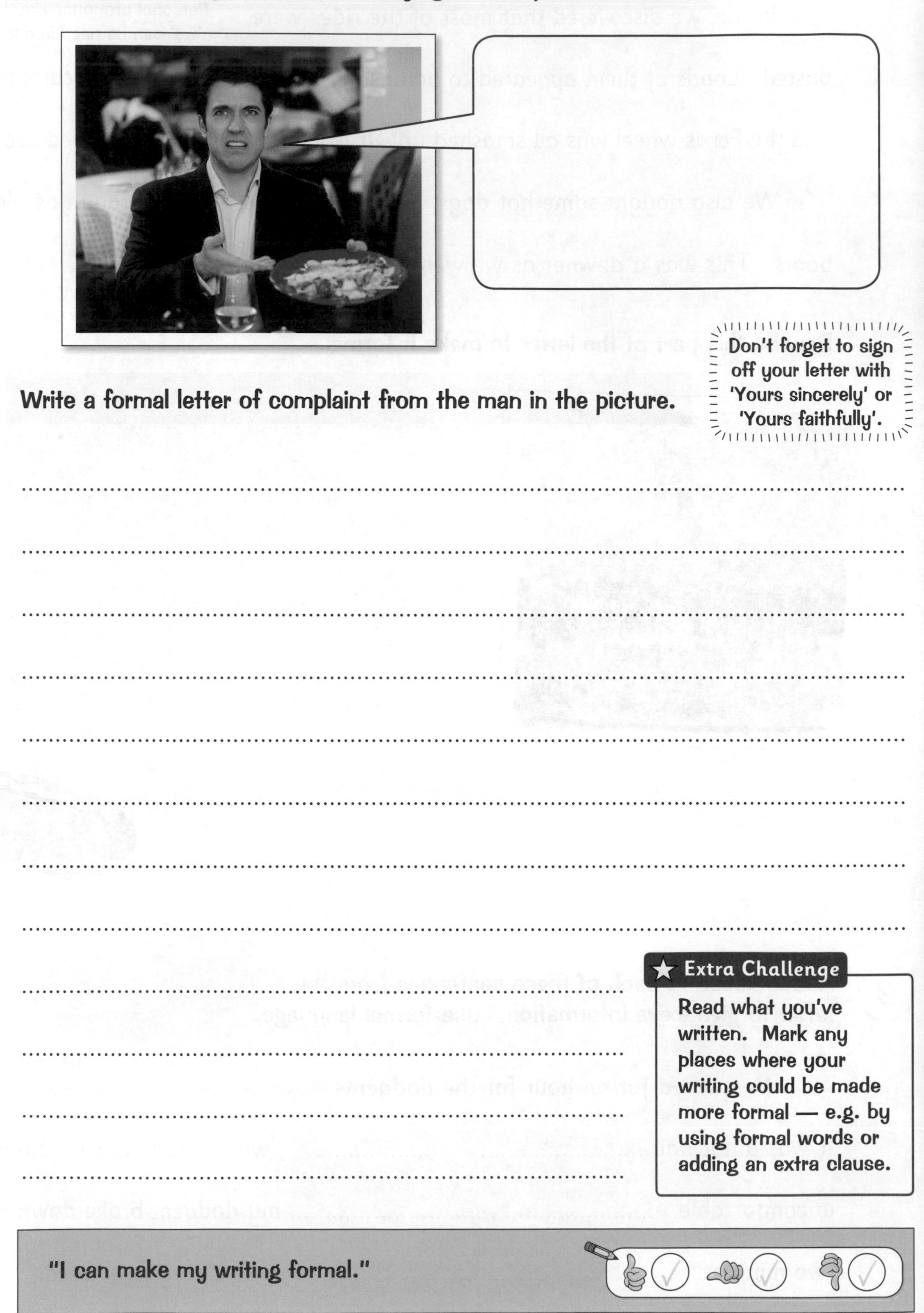

Write a formal letter of complaint from the man in the picture.

Don't forget to sign off your letter with 'Yours sincerely' or 'Yours faithfully'.

....

....

....

....

....

....

....

....

....

....

....

....

★ Extra Challenge

Read what you've written. Mark any places where your writing could be made more formal — e.g. by using formal words or adding an extra clause.

"I can make my writing formal."

Mayhem at the Museum

You can use dialogue to make some non-fiction texts, such as newspaper reports, more detailed and engaging. Dialogue is what a person says and how they say it.

You can use direct speech or reported speech in your writing.

Key Terms

- **Direct speech** is the exact words a person says. It uses speech marks. — e.g. "I've lost my plate of Brussels sprouts," said Cyril.
- **Reported speech** is when you write what a person says in your own words. — e.g. Cyril said that he had lost his plate of Brussels sprouts.

1 **This is the opening to a newspaper report about a strange event at a museum. Circle the direct speech and underline the reported speech.**

Visitors to the Plumpley Museum of Oddities were left stunned yesterday after a number of exhibits came to life. Museum curator Theophile P. Hodges told reporters that a model of a rare type of hairless mammoth, the skeleton of a six-legged snake and a selection of Roman sunglasses were amongst the items that developed a life of their own. "It was most peculiar," declared Hodges.

Explain how the use of speech improves the text.

Think about what the speech adds to the extract.

....

....

....

2 **Rewrite the extract below using direct speech.**

You could use direct speech to make the extract more interesting.

Visitors saw some strange things happening. Violet Stynk, 89, saw a fossilised squid come to life. Her sister Flo, 92, was chased by skeleton bats.

....

....

....

....

....

....

3 **This extract uses lots of direct speech. Rewrite it using reported speech so that the information is summarised briefly but accurately.**

Museum owner Ignatius Hobbs said, "Nobody was hurt, thankfully. No scrapes or bruises on anyone. Also, people enjoyed seeing the exhibits come to life! We think it was caused by a cursed Egyptian burial mask. Well, that's what the mask claims. Spooky stuff! Still, the important thing is that all the visitors had a great time. We might make it an annual event."

....

....

....

....

....

4. **Continue the newspaper report by describing how staff, visitors and exhibits reacted to the event. Use direct speech and reported speech in your writing.**

You could use direct speech to add detail about what happened and how people felt.

What might the people in this photo say? How might they speak?

You could use reported speech to summarise people's reactions.

How might staff and visitors in the museum react?

....

....

....

....

....

....

....

....

....

....

....

....

★ Extra Challenge

Write a newspaper report about the opening of an odd new exhibit at the museum. Include direct and reported speech.

"I can use speech in my writing."

Theseus and the Minotaur

Writers can move the action of a story forward using dialogue — instead of just describing what's happening, they can have the characters explain it. For example, "I'm running as fast as I can" rather than 'He ran quickly'.

The dialogue you use in your writing can change the atmosphere of the story.

Key Terms

- Dialogue is what a character says and how they say it. — e.g. "I can do this," said Richard eagerly.
- Atmosphere is the feeling of a piece of writing — for example, spooky, funny, sad. — e.g. "Will nobody help me?" asked Helen sorrowfully. This has a sad tone.

1. **This is an extract from the beginning of a myth. Read the extract and complete the task below.**

"It is time to send more young Athenians to be eaten by the Minotaur," lamented King Aegeus. "Will his appetite ever be satisfied?"

As the tributes prepared to board the boat, Theseus yelled, "Stop! The Minotaur shall kill no more. I will sail to Crete and slay the beast."

"You're a man of great courage," Aegeus exclaimed with a smile. "Take this sword and save us from the monster."

"My thanks," said Theseus, bowing. "Now, my lord, please untie the rope and I'll raise the sail. Farewell."

Underline the dialogue that moves the story forward.

★ Extra Challenge

Rewrite the extract, describing what's happening instead of using dialogue. What differences do you notice between the two pieces of writing?

2 **When Theseus arrives in Crete, the princess Ariadne falls in love with him and offers to help him. Rewrite the extract using dialogue to move the story forward.**

Ariadne told Theseus that even if he defeated the Minotaur, there was no guarantee he would survive. The labyrinth, the Minotaur's lair, was a winding maze that none had escaped. Theseus was discouraged, but Ariadne gave him a ball of thread. With it, Theseus could mark a trail through the labyrinth.

3 **Theseus crosses the labyrinth and discovers the Minotaur at its heart. The words in bold create different types of atmosphere for the extract. Decide what atmosphere you want the extract to have and circle the appropriate options.**

"Foul beast, I'm here to put an end to your wickedness," Theseus cried.

"I've been **slaying Athenians / trapped here** for many years," replied the Minotaur **fiercely / mournfully**. "I **regret / rejoice** that you will not escape."

"I have friends to help me," Theseus said. "Unlike you, vile creature."

"Enough of your **pathetic / hurtful** words," the Minotaur **sobbed / roared**. "If you wish to fight me, I'll **reluctantly / happily** kill you as I did the others."

4 **Rewrite the dialogue below to match the atmosphere in brackets.**

The first one has been done for you.

"The Minotaur is hideous," Aegeus said. (funny)

"The Minotaur is uglier than the palace lavatories," Aegeus chuckled.

"I will stop the Minotaur," Theseus said. (dramatic)

....

"I think you can do it, Theseus," Ariadne said. (confident)

....

"I will eat you," the Minotaur said. (threatening)

....

5 **Theseus beats the Minotaur, escapes and finds Ariadne. Using dialogue to move the story forward and create a suitable atmosphere, describe their escape from Crete.**

Think about how Theseus and Ariadne escape from Crete.

What will the atmosphere be? Is it tense or exciting?

What might Theseus and Ariadne say? How do they speak?

....

....

....

....

....

....

....

....

....

"I can use dialogue to move the story forward and change the atmosphere of a text."

Beyond the Stars

Writers can shape how their characters come across to the reader by using dialogue (what a character says and how they say it).

You can use informal language, such as chatty words and contractions, to make direct speech sound more realistic.

You can describe how characters speak using verbs and adverbs.

How characters act also affects how they come across.

Key Terms

- Direct speech is the exact words a character says. e.g. "Where's my frog?" asked Karen.
- Informal language is chatty — it's how people often talk to their friends. e.g. "He's having a kip," replied Mr Poe.
- Contractions are words that are joined together to make a shorter word. e.g. where's = where + is, he's = he + is
- Verbs are doing or being words. e.g. "I need him!" exclaimed Karen.
- Adverbs often describe verbs. e.g. "Wake up, Bert!" she yelled impatiently.

1 **This is an extract from a science fiction story about a team of astronauts on a mission to outer space. Read the extract, then complete the task below.**

Shima gave Tom a quick thumbs up, adjusted her harness and grinned. "I'm all sorted," she said. "You doing OK?" Tom nodded. "Awesome," Shima continued, "then let's split. Control, how long until we're cleared for take-off?"

"It won't be long now, Commander Khatri," came the voice over the speaker system.

Underline the contractions and circle any other informal language in the dialogue.

Fill in the table to show what each example suggests about Shima's personality.

Example	What it shows
Shima gave Tom a quick thumbs up	
let's split	
Control, how long until we're cleared for take-off?	

2 **In the next part of the story, Shima and Tom search for the mysterious planet Fedra. The words in bold create two different impressions of Tom's character. Decide how you want him to come across and circle the appropriate options.**

When you write a story, it's important that your characters are consistent — for example, they don't suddenly change from kind to cruel or shy to outgoing for no reason.

"Four months in space," **whined / chuckled** Tom, "and still our search goes on." He folded his arms and **smiled / scowled** at Shima.

"Hang on," said Shima, pointing to a distant speck. "What's that?"

"Who knows?" Tom said **cheerfully / wearily**. "The fact is that Fedra **doesn't exist / is very nearby**, so we're **definitely / never** going to find it. We should just **give up now / keep looking**."

Tom leaned back in his chair and closed his eyes. "I wonder when we'll see Earth again," he said **bitterly / hopefully**.

3 **Add a word or phrase to each gap to show Tom's and Shima's reactions when they realise that they have found Fedra.**

"I don't believe it!" Tom yelled ...., his boredom forgotten.

"................................." cried Shima. "Let's get down there and explore!"

Grabbing the controls, Shima steered the space shuttle towards the planet.

"Careful," .... Tom, "watch out for those mountains."

"Don't sweat it," .... Shima as the landscape below them came into sharp focus, ".."

4 **Describe Shima and Tom's first moments on Fedra. Include dialogue between them and develop their characters by showing how they talk and act.**

Shima and Tom stepped down the ramp, gazing in wonder.

Think about how you want Shima and Tom to come across.

....

....

....

....

....

....

How will they talk? What might they say?

....

....

....

....

"I can use dialogue to develop characters."

The Path Through the Wood

We call the feeling of a story its atmosphere. For example, a ghost story will be more effective if it has a spooky atmosphere.

A lot of atmosphere comes from descriptions. You can make your descriptions more effective by choosing your adjectives, verbs and adverbs carefully.

Grammar Guide

Nouns name things.	e.g. the dog
Adjectives describe nouns.	e.g. the smelly dog
Verbs are doing or being words.	e.g. the smelly dog ran
Adverbs often describe verbs.	e.g. the smelly dog ran quickly

1. **This is an extract from the beginning of a fantasy story. Underline the verbs, adjectives and adverbs that create a happy atmosphere.**

It had rained heavily overnight, but luckily the day dawned fresh and bright. John headed into the palace gardens, eager to breathe in the sweet scent of the vibrant flowers. He gazed joyfully up at the cloudless sapphire sky and grinned. It was a perfect day to travel to the market to buy food for the Queen's griffins.

2. **Read the next part of the story below and complete the task on the next page.**

In the distance, he could see a footpath winding enticingly across the lush fields. As he opened the gate, an ominous chill crept over him. To reach the market, he would have to pass through the deep, shadowy woods.

Fill in the table to describe what atmosphere each example creates.

Example	What atmosphere it creates
a footpath winding enticingly	
deep, shadowy woods	

3 **John walks some way through the woods and comes out in a clearing. Fill in the gaps with adjectives and adverbs so that the extract has a magical atmosphere.**

On the far side of the clearing, John could see a ....

door set into the side of a .... tree. The door glinted

.... in the .... light of the lantern

that hung above it. John stared

.... as the door

swung .... towards

him and a ....

opening appeared before him.

Rewrite the extract to give it a creepy atmosphere.

You can change the extract as much as you want.

....

....

....

....

....

4 John goes through the door and it closes behind him. He comes out in a snowy glade where he sees a fox. Continue the story, describing the fox and the new setting to create a particular atmosphere.

Think about what atmosphere you want to create — e.g. mysterious, scary, cheerful.

Think about what adjectives you could use to create atmosphere.

How might John and the fox act?

Think about how to use verbs and adverbs to describe the characters' actions and add to the atmosphere.

....

....

....

....

....

....

....

....

....

....

....

....

★ Extra Challenge

What happens next? If you have time, finish the story. Remember to plan before you start writing.

"I can create an effective atmosphere for a story."

The Pyramid

How you structure your writing is important — you can change the structure to make it easier to understand, more interesting or more exciting for the reader.

You can put the events of your story in chronological order, or you can use techniques like flashbacks. Cliffhangers can help to build excitement.

Key Terms

- Chronological order is when events are organised in the order they occur. e.g. I was woken by my alarm. I leapt out of bed and pulled on my uniform.
- A flashback is when the story shifts from the present to the past. e.g. The smell of hay transported me back to my eighth birthday...
- A cliffhanger is when a section of writing ends in a way that creates suspense. e.g. The bus veered wildly towards the lake; it would never stop in time.

1 **These are the parts of a story set in Ancient Egypt.**

Boy lives in the desert | There is an accident. | Boy is captured.

Boy helps to build a pyramid. | Boy runs away. | Boy is bullied.

Plan one story with a logical order using the parts above. Include a flashback.

1. ....
2. ....
3. ....
4. ....
5. ....
6. ....

Explain why you included a flashback where you did.

....

....

....

★ Extra Challenge

Plan a different story that includes a flashback. It could be set in Ancient Egypt or another time or place in history. If you have time, you could write the full story.

2 **This is the beginning of one version of the story. Carry on the extract so that it includes a cliffhanger.**

Remember, a cliffhanger should create suspense for the reader.

Menna staggered, his fingers slipping on the heavy stone he was carrying. With a grunt, he set it down. He rubbed his sore muscles and gazed at the half-built pyramid. Teams of slaves inched up its side, dragging huge boulders.

....

©iStock.com/ nihatdursun

....

....

....

....

★ Extra Challenge

Carry on the story so it leads into the next extract.

3 **Later in the story, Menna thinks back to his capture by slave traders. Read the extract, and then explain why you think the writer included this flashback.**

Think about how the flashback makes you feel.

Menna's mind drifted. He was lying on the bank of the Nile, his head resting in his mother's lap. Her drowsy lullaby stopped suddenly, and Menna became aware of the pounding of hooves. His mother scrambled to her feet and ran, dragging him with her. Before they could reach the shelter of the nearby trees, the horsemen were upon them. Menna felt himself seized and hauled onto the back of the nearest horse.

....

....

4 **In the next part of the story, Menna is bullied by his master, Bek. Read the extract and then write a flashback describing Menna's first meeting with Bek.**

A sudden slap to his head sent Menna sprawling forwards onto his hands and knees. "Get back to work, you lazy worm!" bellowed Bek.

Menna lurched to his feet. Month after month, year after year he had put up with Bek's cruelty. He remembered the first time they had met.

....

....

....

....

Think about how you want Bek to come across — is he rude or violent?

5 **Write the end of the story, in which Menna escapes. Include a cliffhanger and a flashback in your writing.**

You could use a cliffhanger to make it seem as if Menna might not escape.

....

....

....

....

....

....

You could use a flashback to describe a previous escape attempt.

....

....

....

"I can structure my writing to make it interesting and exciting for the reader."

The Detective's Father

Writers need to describe the settings and characters in their stories effectively so readers can picture the places and people in their heads.

You can use similes, metaphors and personification to make your settings and characters lifelike and memorable. Language which appeals to the senses can also help to make your writing more realistic for the reader.

Key Terms

- A **simile** describes one thing as being similar to another. e.g. The rabbit's eyes were as black as night.
- A **metaphor** describes something by saying it is something else. e.g. The rabbit's eyes were black marbles.
- **Personification** uses human qualities to describe something that's not human. e.g. The pen danced across the page.
- **Appeals to the senses** are descriptions of sight, hearing, touch, taste or smell. e.g. I bit hungrily into the sweet, juicy pear.

Similes often use the words 'like' or 'as'. Metaphors don't.

1 **Read this extract from a mystery story. Fill in the table with two examples from the extract that appeal to the senses, and explain how they make you feel.**

Katrina collapses into her leather chair and wipes her hot, sweaty forehead. As she takes a sip of cool, sweet grape juice, her heart rate slows. Glancing at her messy desk, Katrina spots a creased brown envelope. She opens it, and the musty smell of damp floats off the letter inside. 'Come to my hideout if you want to see your father again.' Katrina's sharp gasp hangs in the air.

Example	Sense it appeals to	How it makes you feel

2 **Katrina works out where the hideout is and goes to investigate. Read the extract below and fill in the gaps, using appeals to the senses to describe the hideout.**

Think about the atmosphere you want to create.

The stairs are uneven beneath Katrina's feet, forcing her to lean on the stone walls, which are .... to the touch. The wind .... behind Katrina, carrying with it the taste of .... Katrina hurries up the crooked staircase towards a .... door, which is slightly ajar. The smell of .... from inside makes Katrina recoil. There's the sudden sound of .... from within...

3 **Katrina goes inside and finds herself in a narrow, stone passage. Using the techniques in brackets, rewrite the sentences below to describe the scene.**

The lamps are dim. (personification)

....

The floor is dusty. (simile)

....

The air is cold. (metaphor)

....

Katrina's feet thud against the floor. (simile)

....

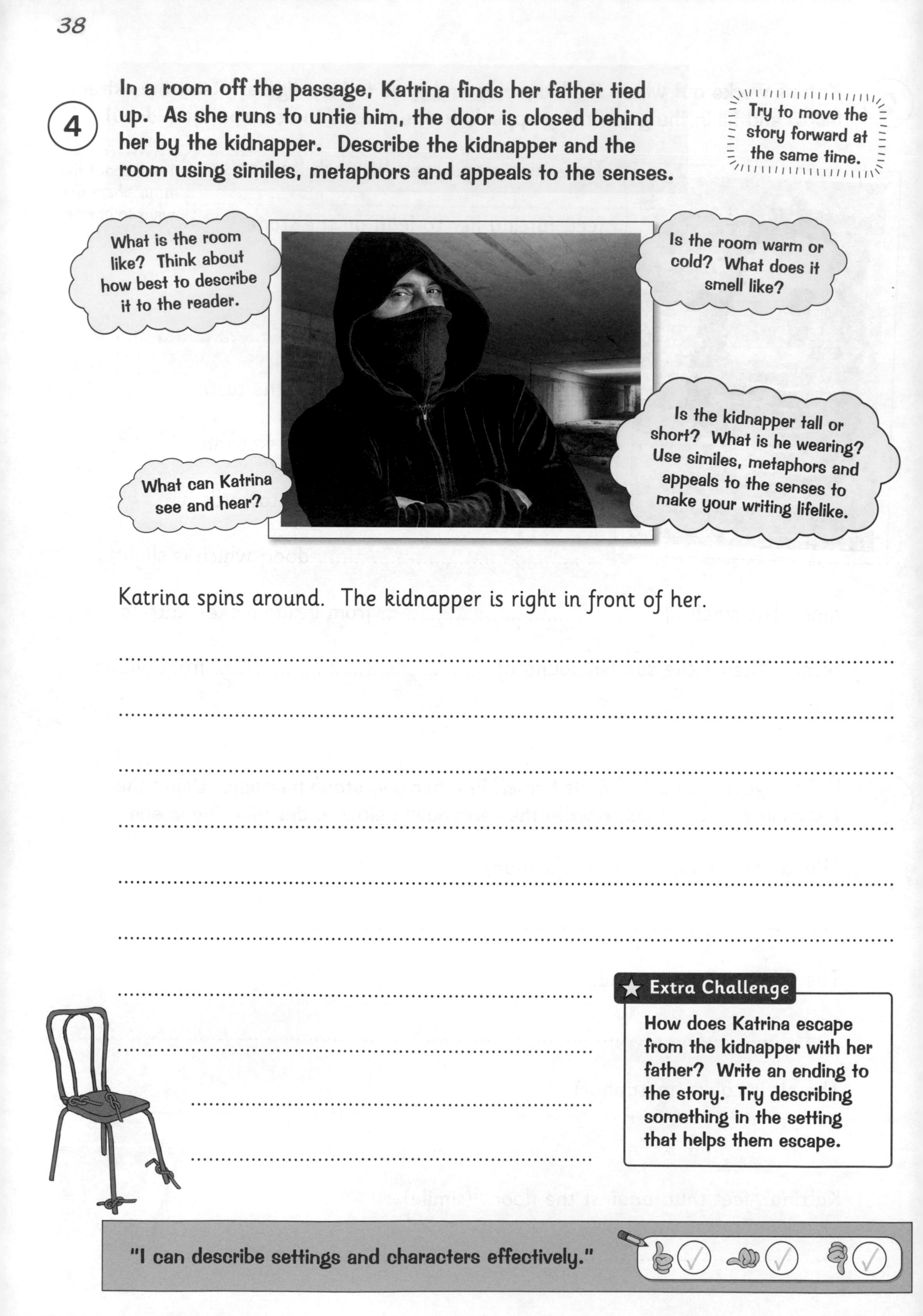

4 In a room off the passage, Katrina finds her father tied up. As she runs to untie him, the door is closed behind her by the kidnapper. Describe the kidnapper and the room using similes, metaphors and appeals to the senses.

Try to move the story forward at the same time.

Katrina spins around. The kidnapper is right in front of her.

....

....

....

....

....

....

....

....

....

....

★ Extra Challenge

How does Katrina escape from the kidnapper with her father? Write an ending to the story. Try describing something in the setting that helps them escape.

"I can describe settings and characters effectively."

Songs of the Sea

We call the feeling of a poem its atmosphere — e.g. it could be happy, sad or angry. A poem's atmosphere affects how it makes the reader feel.

You can change a poem's atmosphere by changing its rhyme scheme and rhythm, or by using language techniques like alliteration, onomatopoeia and imagery.

Key Terms

Words rhyme if they end with the same sound. Rhythm is the pattern of sounds in a poem.	e.g. 'Drumming rain on the window pane' has two rhyming words and a strong rhythm.
Alliteration is when words begin with the same sound.	e.g. Water whirled down the waste pipe.
Onomatopoeia is when a word sounds like the thing it is describing.	e.g. My boots squelched and slurped in the mud.
Imagery is language that creates a picture in your head.	e.g. Rain pummelled the glass like tiny fists.

Imagery includes similes and metaphors — there's more about these on p.36.

1 **Read this extract from a poem about a storm at sea and underline the alliterative words. Explain what effect alliteration has in the first or second line of the extract.**

The seething sea sweeps across the sands,

Waves grab and grip like grasping hands.

....

....

★ Extra Challenge

Write down as many sea-related words that alliterate with the word 'waves' as you can in two minutes.

Add alliterative words to the sentences below.

You can use more than one word in a gap.

The dolphin dived down to the .... depths.

Schools of salmon .... in the sunlight.

The creepy cave was concealed by ....

The turning tide .... over Tilly's toes.

Seaweed .... in the .... sea.

2 **This is an extract from a different poem. Read the extract and underline all the onomatopoeic words.**

I stomp along the jagged cliff, with

The muted boom of waves far below me.

Rowdy gulls shriek above my head, while

Around me the wind whispers and moans.

Think about what atmosphere the onomatopoeic words create.

Add onomatopoeic words to the sentences below to give them a happy, carefree atmosphere.

The gentle breeze .... in the sand dunes.

The crab dropped into the rock pool with a ....

The .... of the ice cream van brought children running.

3 **Add imagery to the gaps below to complete each sentence.**

Make your images as interesting as you can.

Sunbathers dot the beach like ....

The smell of sun cream is as .... as ....

The foaming ocean was like ....

Rewrite each sentence below so it contains a simile or metaphor.

See p. 36 for more on similes and metaphors.

The sandcastle is very tall.

....

Children splash in the sea.

....

Turtles swim around the reef.

....

4 **Read the poem below and underline all the rhyming words. Write a poem that has the same rhyme scheme and the same number of beats per line.**

Words like cat, sheep and boat have lots of rhymes.

Young Jeremy Moore ....

Went down to the shore ....

To watch the seaweed grow. ....

Then came a big swell ....

That made Jerry yell ....

And wet him from top to toe. ....

5 **Using the photo below, write your own poem about the sea.**

Do you want your poem to have a rhyme scheme?

Use imagery to make your descriptions vivid.

How might you use alliteration or onomatopoeia?

....

....

....

....

....

....

....

....

....

....

"I can use language techniques to write effective poems."

Answers

Pages 3-5 — Planning Your Work

1. You should have joined the extracts like this:

   Extract 1 — Purpose: To advise — Audience: Teenagers

   Extract 2 — Purpose: To entertain — Audience: Children

   Extract 3 — Purpose: To persuade — Audience: Adults
2. You should have joined the texts to the following writing styles:

   A newspaper article informing readers about a war. — Formal, serious language, lots of information.

   An email telling your best friend about your holiday. — Informal language, personal tone.

   A story about a night in a haunted house. — Descriptive language, building suspense.
3. Any sensible order, for example:
   - Introduction
   - Earliest castles
   - Late Medieval castles
   - Decline of castles
   - Conclusion
4. Any suitable points to complete the plan. For example:
   - Lian goes into the shed and finds a hole in the back wall.
   - She sees a baby rabbit cowering next to a pile of flower pots that have been knocked over.
   - She uses carrot pieces to entice the rabbit out of the shed.
   - She sees the rabbit run off with its family.
5. Any suitable points to complete the plan. For example:
   - Paragraph 1 — Details about the dog.
   - Paragraph 2 — Witness statement — neighbour heard barking and saw a dark shape in garden.
   - Paragraph 3 — Owner's statement — upset and shocked. Plea for safe return.

   Any suitable purpose and audience. For example:

   Purpose — To inform / To entertain
   Audience — Local residents / Adults

Pages 6-7 — Editing Your Work

1. You should have used the suggestions to make the edited extract more interesting. Here are some examples of the types of changes you might have made:
   - Starting the story with action, e.g. 'Bill sauntered down the dusty road towards school, kicking a football in front of him.'
   - Describing the setting and cat, e.g. 'Crouched on a rickety wooden fence was a large, ginger cat with sea-green eyes.'
   - Showing Bill's surprise, e.g. 'Bill's mouth dropped open, and he rubbed his eyes in disbelief.'
2. You should have made suggestions to make the extract more interesting. Here are some parts of the extract that you could have suggested changing:
   - 'One day...' — this opening could be made more interesting and original, e.g. by giving more detail about what Bill is doing.
   - 'a fluffy cat' — the cat could be described in more detail to create a more vivid picture for the reader.
   - 'Bill stopped and looked at the cat and it looked back at him' — this could be reworded to avoid the repetition of 'looked', and to give a clearer impression of how the cat is looking at Bill (e.g. glaring, peering curiously).
3. You should have made suggestions to make the extract clearer and easier to read. Here are some parts of the extract that you could have suggested changing:
   - The first two sentences could be combined and/or rewritten to avoid repetition of 'Great Barrier Reef'.
   - 'Lots of fish... sharks and fish' — these sentences could be joined using a linking word or phrase (e.g. 'such as' or 'including') to help the text flow. One of the references to 'fish' should be removed to prevent repetition.
   - The final paragraph could be combined with the first paragraph because they both give information about the size of the Great Barrier Reef.

Page 8 — Proofreading Your Work

1. These are the errors you should have marked and corrected in the text:

   Deer (Dear) Miss Henshaw,

   We would like to invite you to visit our school and give a **tolk (talk)** to our class. Everyone in our class **love (loves)** your **book's (books)**, **espesially (especially)** the 'Broken Wings' series. We have been doing a project based on the

Answers

first 'Broken Wings' book **(, / — / brackets around 'Flying Free')** 'Flying Free'. **We prefer it than (We prefer it to / We like it more than)** any other book, and we have learnt a lot about flying machines**(.)**

So, why should you visit us. **(?)** You should visit because we will make you feel really welcome, with handmade banners and **an (a)** delicious lunch in our **cantine (canteen)**. We **had (have)** planned lots of **activites (activities)** so you will have a **wonderfull (wonderful)** day. **furthermore (Furthermore)**, you have inspired us **too (to)** write our own stories, and we would be overjoyed to have the chance to share them with **u (you)**.

Your visit would **have made (make)** us elated, excited and motivated to keep **writeing (writing)**. So please consider coming to visit**, (;)** it would make our year!

Your (Yours) sincerely,
Class 6B

Pages 9-11 — All About Volcanoes

1. You should have underlined these facts:

   'Active volcanoes are found all around the world', 'there are none in the UK', 'in my lifetime alone, they have caused destruction in many countries', 'lots of tourists visit them'.

   Any suitable rewriting of the text that uses only facts and has an objective tone. For example:

   Active volcanoes are found all around the world, although there are none in the UK. In recent years, volcanoes have caused destruction in many countries. However, lots of tourists visit them.
2. Any suitable words. For example:
   Many volcanoes are located in inhabited areas, so when they erupt they **often** cause a lot of destruction. **In many cases**, lava flows and falling debris destroy buildings and kill people. Plants and animals close to volcanoes are also **frequently** harmed by eruptions.
3. You should have circled:

   Ash cloud, Crater, Magma chamber, Main vent, Lava flow, Secondary vent.

   Your writing should be clear and informative, and include the following features:
   - A logical structure, e.g. describing the different parts of a volcano from the bottom upwards.
   - Technical terms from the diagram, e.g. 'The magma chamber sits beneath the volcano.'
   - Objective language, e.g. 'The crater is located at the top of the volcano.'
4. You should have written a clear, well-structured and factual report. For example:
   - You should have used generalisations, e.g. '**Many** of the world's active volcanoes are found in the Ring of Fire in the Pacific Ocean.'
   - You should have used technical terms, e.g. 'Volcanoes generally occur along **plate margins**.'
   - You writing should have an objective tone, e.g. 'Of the 1500 active volcanoes on Earth, Mauna Loa in Hawaii is the largest that is above water.'

Pages 12-14 — How Rainbows Are Formed

1. You should have underlined any nouns that break up the flow of the text. For example:

   Have you ever wondered how rainbows appear in the sky as **rainbows** do? Do you want to know why **rainbows** need rain to get **rainbows'** colours or the role sunlight plays in forming **rainbows**? If so, read on to learn what a rainbow is and how a **rainbow** is formed.

   Any suitable rewriting of the extract that uses pronouns where appropriate. For example:

   Have you ever wondered how rainbows appear in the sky as **they** do? Do you want to know why **they** need rain to get **their** colours or the role sunlight plays in forming **them**? If so, read on to learn what a rainbow is and how **it** is formed.
2. You should have filled in the gaps like this:

   Rainbows appear **in the sky** when sunlight passes through water droplets. Beams of light that come **from the sun** are **initially** white, but this white light is made up of many different colours. **When** the white light passes through water, it slows down and scatters **in different directions**. This causes the different colours to become visible.
3. You should have circled:

   As a result, Consequently, However,
   For example, because.
4. You should have written a clear, flowing explanation of how to use the invention.
   For example:
   - You could have started with an introduction that explains what the invention does, e.g. 'The Mindchair allows the user to see through the eyes of any creature on the planet.'

Answers

- You could have then moved on to a logical, step-by-step explanation of how to use the invention, e.g. 'First, the user pulls the red lever to lower the steps to the chair. Next, they climb into the chair.'
- You should have used pronouns and linking words and phrases to make the text flow, e.g. 'The user fits the headset over **their** eyes so **they** can pick a creature's eyes to see through. **In addition**, the headset allows the user to hear through the creature's ears.'
- You should have used adverbials to add extra information, e.g. 'The user can choose to view a different creature on the headset by tapping **twice in quick succession**.'

Pages 15-17 — Should Schools Ban Unhealthy Food?

1. You should have underlined:
   It is also delicious, Those people are wrong: children should have the freedom to make their own decisions about their diet.
   Any suitable rewriting of the text that changes opinions to facts. For example:
   Unhealthy food is often high in salt, sugar and fat. **Many people continue to eat it because they enjoy the taste.** Some people think that schools should not serve unhealthy food because it can cause health problems and encourage poor eating habits. **Others believe that** children should have the freedom to make their own decisions about their diet.
2. Any suitable linking words and phrases.
   For example:
   It is widely known that a poor diet can have a negative effect on health. **For example,** too much salt can cause high blood pressure, increasing the risk of heart disease. **Similarly,** a diet high in sugar can cause tooth decay and may contribute to liver damage.
   However, if unhealthy food is banned in schools, children may simply eat more of it outside of school. **It could be argued that** it would be better if they learnt to eat unhealthy food in small quantities, rather than it being banned entirely.
3. Any suitable counter-argument that opposes the argument put across. For example:
   - Children who are encouraged to choose healthy food at school (rather than having no option) may be more likely to choose healthy food outside of school.
   - Some children do not like fruit and vegetables and may not eat them, regardless of how much they are encouraged to do so.
4. Your writing should be well-structured and fact-based. You should have used linking words and phrases to help the text flow. For example:
   - You could have structured your text by giving an argument, then giving a counter-argument, e.g. 'Unhealthy food is often high in fat, so banning it in schools may help to prevent children becoming obese. However, some people believe that if children are not allowed to make their own decisions about what they eat from an early age, they will be unable to make good dietary decisions as adults.'
   - You could have brought in specific facts, e.g. 'Studies show that childhood obesity is linked to health problems such as high blood pressure, so banning unhealthy food in schools may improve children's health.'
   - You should have used linking words and phrases to connect your points, e.g. 'Some people believe that children have the right to make their own decisions about their diet. **In contrast**, others believe that young children are unable to understand the importance of a healthy diet.'

Pages 18-20 — A Letter of Complaint

1. You should have circled:
   My friend and I, an unpleasant, To begin with, a long time, very, reached, irritable, tainted our enjoyment of.
2. You should have underlined:
   busted, Loads, all smashed up, stuff, as tough as old boots, downer, proper
   Any suitable rewriting of the text. For example:
   Inside, we discovered that most of the rides were **not working**. **Many** of them appeared to be unsafe: we noticed rust on the carousel, and the Ferris wheel was **badly damaged**. It is vital that **all rides** be repaired soon.
   We also bought some hot dogs, which turned out to be **repulsively tough and chewy**. This was **very disappointing** as we were **extremely** hungry.
3. Any suitable clauses. For example:
   We queued for an hour for the dodgems, **which was very unpleasant**. It was a hot day **and there was no shade**, which made our wait more uncomfortable. **Once we got onto the ride**, my dodgem broke down after two minutes. **As this is our favourite ride**, we were very frustrated.

Answers

4. Any suitable suggestions for what the man in the photo could be complaining about, e.g. 'The food is cold.', 'There's too much salt in it.', 'I found a slug in the salad.'

   Your letter should use formal language and be polite and well-structured. For example:
   - It should start with a suitable opening, e.g. 'Dear Mr Higgins' or 'To whom it may concern'.
   - It should use formal language and sentences with multiple clauses, e.g. 'When I attempted to eat the salad, I discovered a large orange slug amongst the rocket leaves, which was extremely off-putting.'
   - It should have a clear structure — you could write a paragraph on each issue, e.g. 'I informed the waiter about the problem with my food, but he merely shrugged. When I requested a replacement meal, he asked me to leave and claimed that I would not be welcome in the restaurant in future. I was deeply upset by his rudeness.'

Pages 21-23 — Mayhem at the Museum

1. You should have circled:

   "It was most peculiar,"

   You should have underlined:

   a model of a rare type of hairless mammoth, the skeleton of a six-legged snake and a selection of Roman sunglasses were amongst the items that developed a life of their own.

   Any explanation of how the use of speech improves the text. For example:
   - Including information from someone who was there makes the events of the article seem more believable.
   - It adds detail to the article, so the reader learns more about what happened.
2. Any suitable rewriting of the extract. For example:

   Violet Stynk, 89, who was visiting the museum with her sister, described the scene: "I was admiring a fossilised squid when it suddenly started wiggling its tentacles."

   Her sister Flo, 92, recounted her own experience: "I was chased around the museum by skeleton bats — it was terrifying."
3. Any suitable rewriting of the extract. For example:

   Museum owner Ignatius Hobbs insisted that nobody was hurt during the day's extraordinary events and maintained that visitors enjoyed the experience. According to Mr Hobbs, a cursed Egyptian burial mask has claimed responsibility. Hobbs is considering making the day's events an annual occurrence.
4. Your writing should be well-structured and informative. You should have used both direct and reported speech to add interest and make it more engaging. For example:
   - You could have used reported speech to summarise people's experience, e.g. 'Molly Coddle, aged 7, told reporters she had befriended a black bear after beating it in a growling match.'
   - You could have used direct speech to show people's thoughts and feelings, e.g. '"I wasn't scared," claimed Miss Coddle. "I've been practising my growling, so I knew I could win."'
   - You could have used a combination of direct and reported speech to describe the reactions of the exhibits to finding themselves alive, e.g. 'Og, aged approximately 50 000, declared that his first action would be to prepare dinner. "Og hungry," he said. "Og build fire. Cook mammoth."'

Pages 24-26 — Theseus and the Minotaur

1. You should have underlined:

   It is time to send more young Athenians to be eaten by the Minotaur, I will sail to Crete and slay the beast, Take this sword and save us from the monster, untie the rope and I'll raise the sail.
2. You should have rewritten the extract to include suitable dialogue which makes the important plot points clear. For example:
   - Ariadne telling Theseus about the Minotaur's lair, e.g. '"Even if you defeat the Minotaur, you still have to escape the labyrinth, and no one has ever done that," Ariadne explained.'
   - Theseus expressing his feelings and trying to find a solution, e.g. '"How will I fulfil my duty to my King now?" Theseus cried in horror. "Is there no way out of the labyrinth, Ariadne?"'
   - Ariadne giving the ball of thread to Theseus, e.g. '"There is one way to escape," Ariadne said, holding out her hand. "Take this ball of thread. Use it to mark a trail through the labyrinth and follow it back to the exit."'
3. You should have underlined one of the groups of options below to create a consistent atmosphere:

   To create a threatening atmosphere: slaying Athenians, fiercely, rejoice, pathetic, roared, happily.

   To create a sorrowful atmosphere: trapped here, mournfully, regret, hurtful, sobbed, reluctantly.

Answers

4. Any suitable dialogue that matches the atmosphere in brackets. For example:

   Dramatic — e.g. '"I will end the Minotaur's reign of terror," Theseus cried, drawing his sword.'

   Confident — e.g. '"I know you can do it, Theseus," Ariadne declared with conviction.'

   Threatening — e.g. '"I will devour you," the Minotaur growled, licking his lips.'

5. You should have used dialogue to describe Theseus and Ariadne's escape. Here are some techniques you could have used:
   - Setting a suitable and consistent atmosphere using dialogue, e.g. '"You made it out alive! I am thrilled to see you again," Ariadne said, throwing her arms around Theseus.' — this creates a happy atmosphere.
   - Changing the atmosphere to match the story's progression, e.g. '"I am delighted to see you again, but we must leave Crete at once," Theseus whispered without pausing for breath.' — this creates a shift from a happy to an urgent atmosphere.
   - Moving the story forward by having the characters explain what will happen next, e.g. '"Come this way," Ariadne said, taking Theseus's hand. "We can follow this secret passage to the harbour."'

Pages 27-29 — Beyond the Stars

1. You should have underlined:

   I'm, let's, we're, won't.

   You should have circled:

   sorted, You doing OK?, Awesome, let's split.

   Any suitable suggestion. For example:

Example	What it shows
Shima gave Tom a quick thumbs up	She looks after others / tries to cheer them up.
let's split	She is relaxed and informal.
Control, how long until we're cleared for take-off?	She is professional and in control.

2. You should have circled one of the groups of options below to make Tom's character seem consistent:

   To make him seem bad-tempered and negative: whined, scowled, wearily, doesn't exist, never, give up now, bitterly.

   To make him seem lighthearted and positive: chuckled, smiled, cheerfully, is very nearby, definitely, keep looking, hopefully.

3. Any suitable words or phrases. For example:

   "I don't believe it!" Tom yelled **excitedly**, his boredom forgotten.

   "**We've found it!**" cried Shima. "Let's get down there and explore!" Grabbing the controls, Shima steered the space shuttle towards the planet.

   "Careful," **warned** Tom, "watch out for those mountains."

   "Don't sweat it," **grinned** Shima as the landscape below them came into sharp focus, "**I know what I'm doing.**"

4. Your writing should be descriptive and should develop the characters of both Shima and Tom using dialogue and actions. For example:
   - You could develop Shima as the leader of the mission and emphasise her confidence, e.g. '"Mission One to Control," Shima spoke into her headset. "Proceeding to explore Fedra. Over." She turned to Tom. "Come on! Let's explore that lake!"'
   - You could develop Tom's cautious character, e.g. '"We shouldn't go too far from the ship," said Tom uneasily, hanging back as Shima strode ahead. "We don't know what creatures might live here."'

Pages 30-32 — The Path Through the Wood

1. You should have underlined:

   luckily, fresh, bright, eager, sweet, vibrant, joyfully, cloudless, sapphire, grinned, perfect.

2. Any suitable descriptions of atmosphere. For example:

Example	What atmosphere it creates
a footpath winding enticingly	An exciting, adventurous atmosphere
deep, shadowy woods	A tense, menacing atmosphere

3. Any suitable adjectives or adverbs which create a magical atmosphere. For example:

   On the far side of the clearing, John could see a **grand oak** door set into the side of a **towering** tree. The door glinted **radiantly** in the **unearthly** light of the lantern that hung above it. John stared **wide-eyed** as the door swung **gently** towards him and a **glowing** opening appeared before him.